PAGE 1
KU-178-300
PAGES 2-3
PAGES 4-5
PAGES 6-7

PAGES 8-9
PAGES 10-11
PAGES 12-13
PAGES 14-15

Press out your masks.
Ask a grown-up to cut a length of elastic and thread through the two small holes on the sides of the mask.
Then tie two knots in both ends of the elastic to hold the mask in place.
Now your mask is ready!

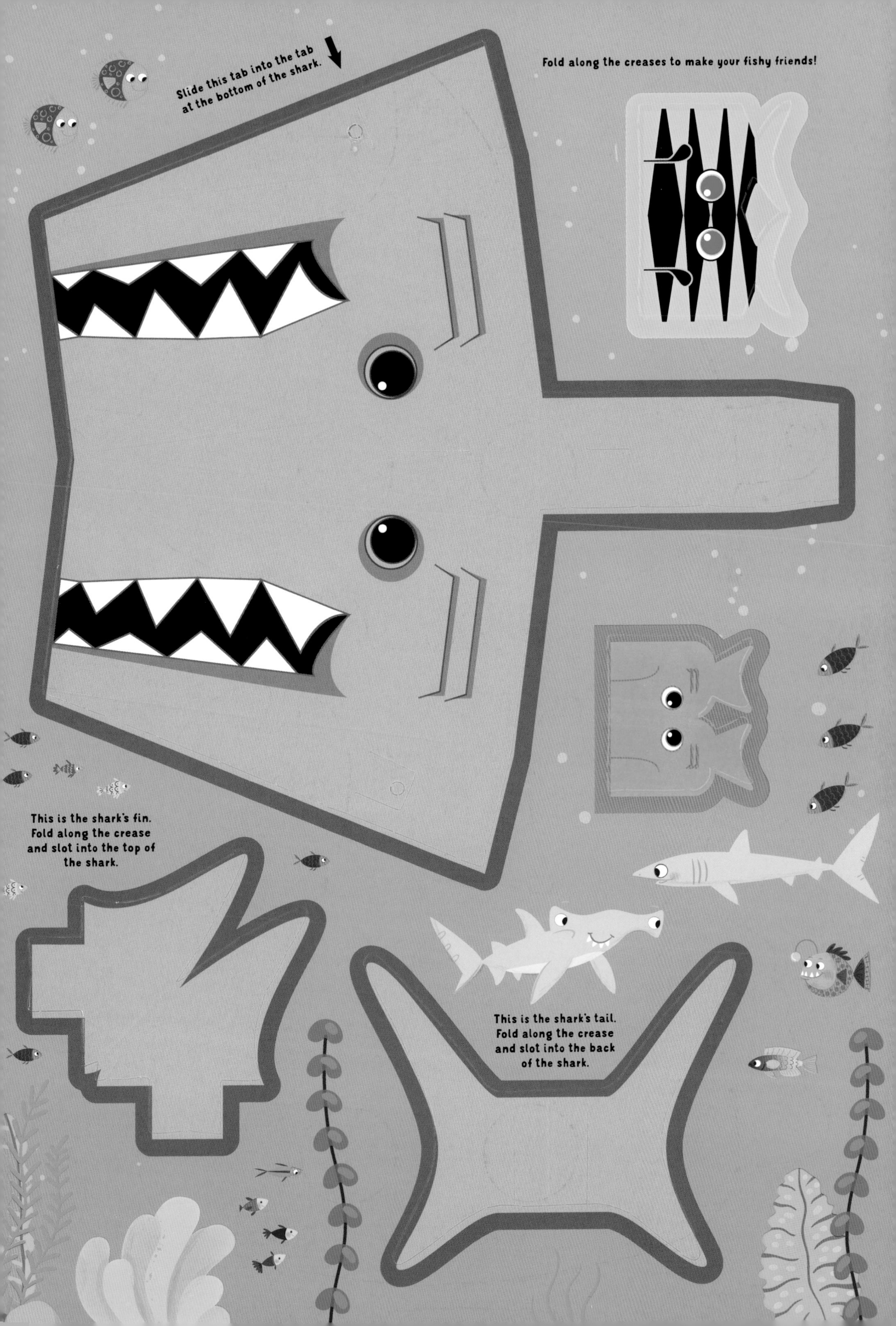
Slide this tab into the tab at the bottom of the shark.
Fold along the creases to make your fishy friends!
This is the shark's fin. Fold along the crease and slot into the top of the shark.
This is the shark's tail. Fold along the crease and slot into the back of the shark.

GOOD MORNING!
The morning sun is rising over the ocean,
and the animals want to play!
Add some happy dolphins splashing in the water.

SUNKEN SHIP!

The deep-sea divers discover a shipwreck full of hidden treasure. Some friendly clown fish and an octopus have come to say 'hello'!

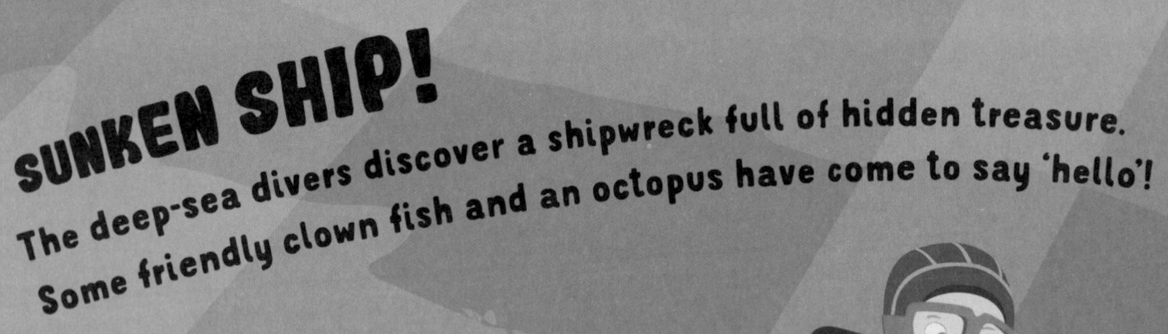

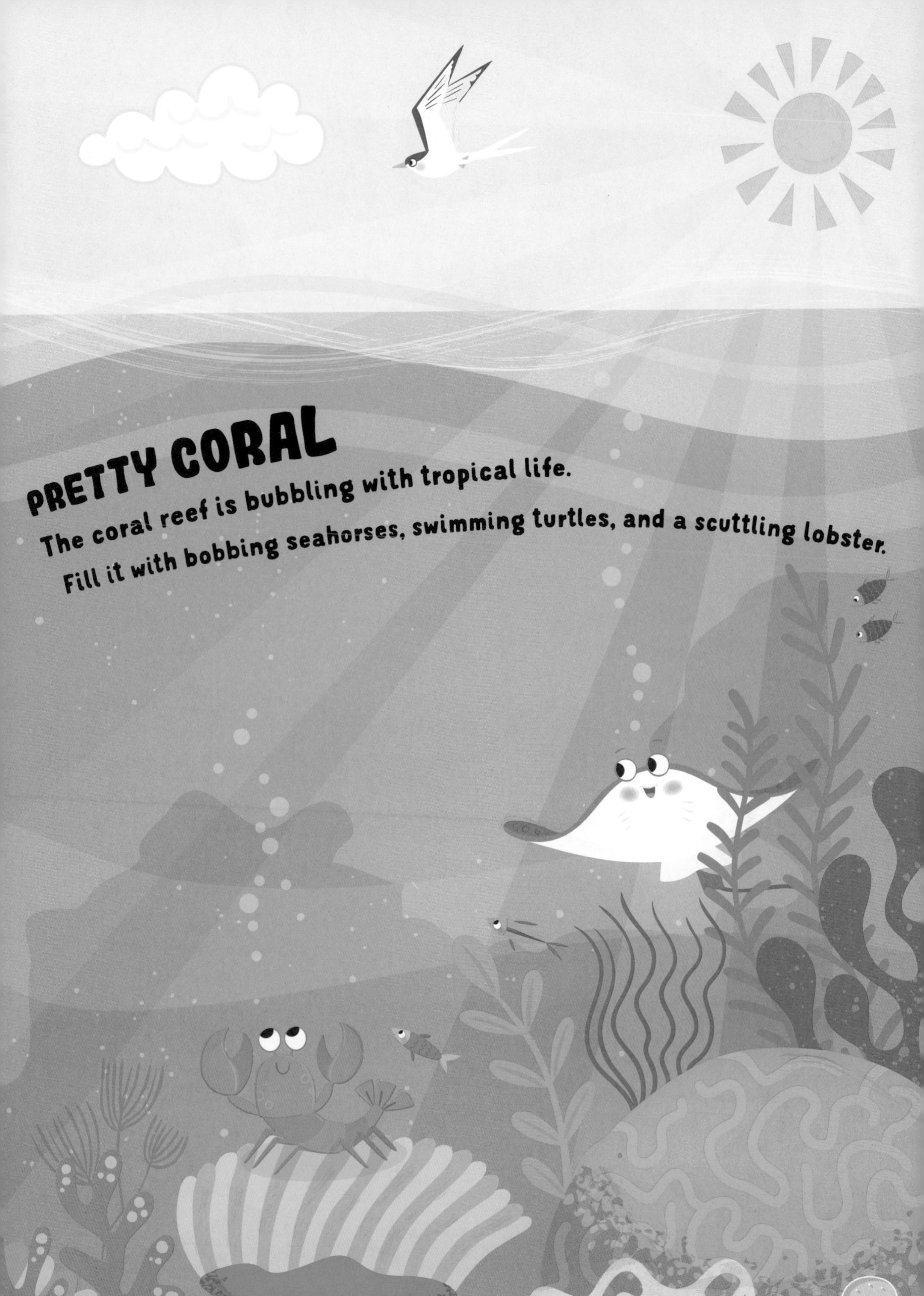

PRETTY CORAL

The coral reef is bubbling with tropical life.

Fill it with bobbing seahorses, swimming turtles, and a scuttling lobster.

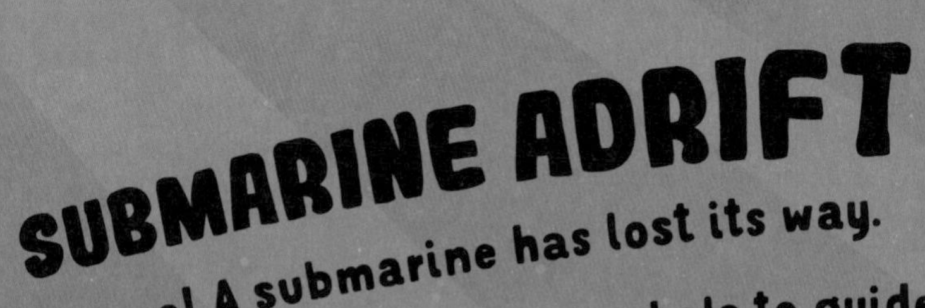

SUBMARINE ADRIFT

Oh, no! A submarine has lost its way.

Add some whales and narwhals to guide it back through the ocean.

The sharks are racing fast, deep under the water.

Add lots of different sharks to the ocean.

FREEZING WATERS

The Arctic Ocean is icy cold, but the sea creatures are ready to have some fun! Add some penguins, seals, and an orca whale.

ROCKPOOL HOME

Lots of small creatures make their home by the rocks.

Fill the rockpool with crabs, mussels, and starfish.

UNDERWATER SPARKS

Deep at the bottom of the ocean,
some creatures light up the water.
Find some glowing jellyfish and octopuses
to light the way for their friends.

FUN FACTS ABOUT CREATURES UNDER THE OCEAN

WHALES breathe through a blowhole on the tops of their heads.

If a **SHARK** loses a tooth, another a tooth, another one grows back ... sometimes in the same day!

An **OCTOPUS** has powerful suckers on each of its eight arms.

PENGUINS have wings, but they can't fly.

Some **CRABS** can only walk sideways!

A **TURTLE** has a tough shell to protect them from predators.